verywhere you look you'll find books to enjoy. Bookworms love to read, and they want to know who wrote the words and who made the pictures for their favorite stories. You will find out in the pages to come. You might even become an author yourself! Follow the bookworm to find some old favorites and exciting new ones in this part of

Acknowledgments appear on page 218.



Printed in the U.S.A.

ISBN: 0-395-51918-7

ABCDEFGHIJ-VH-99876543210

*Senior Author*
John J. Pikulski

*Senior Coordinating Author*
J. David Cooper

*Senior Consulting Author*
William K. Durr

*Coordinating Authors*
Kathryn H. Au
M. Jean Greenlaw
Marjorie Y. Lipson
Susan Page
Sheila W. Valencia
Karen K. Wixson

*Authors*
Rosalinda B. Barrera
Ruth P. Bunyan
Jacqueline L. Chaparro
Jacqueline C. Comas
Alan N. Crawford
Robert L. Hillerich
Timothy G. Johnson
Jana M. Mason
Pamela A. Mason
William E. Nagy
Joseph S. Renzulli
Alfredo Schifini

*Senior Advisor*
Richard C. Anderson

*Advisors*
Christopher J. Baker
Charles Peters



HOUGHTON MIFFLIN COMPANY BOSTON
Atlanta Dallas Geneva, Illinois Palo Alto Princeton Toronto

BOOK 2

BOOK 3

# People Who Write

The world is filled
with wonderful books and
with "bookworms" who
love to read them. But
who are the people who
write the books?
All kinds of people —
that's who!
As you read these
stories and poems, you'll
find out about the people
who wrote the words and
made the pictures.

# CONT

My name is Aliki. I wrote and illustrated the book called *My Five Senses*, which begins on page 14.

Hi! I'm George Shannon. My story, ***The Surprise***, begins on page 32.

We are Jose Aruego and Ariane Dewey. We worked together to make the pictures for ***The Surprise***.

ENTS

My name is Holly Keller. I hope you'll enjoy my story, ***Geraldine's Big Snow***. It begins on page 58.

Hello! I'm Leland Jacobs, and I like to write poetry. In this book, you'll find some of my poems about city life. They begin on page 72.

SHARED READING

# My Five Senses

*by Aliki*

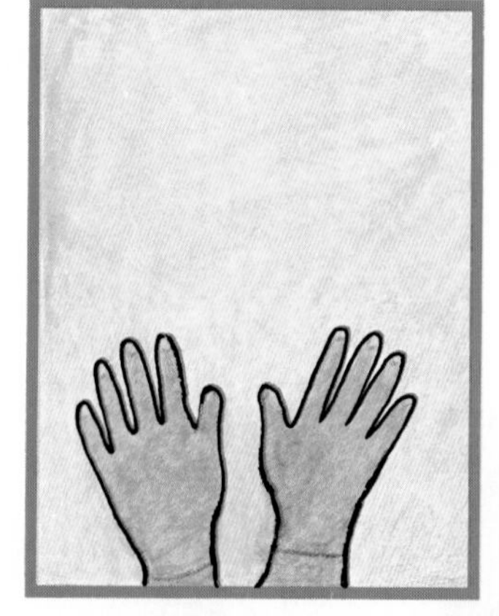

I can see! I see with my eyes.

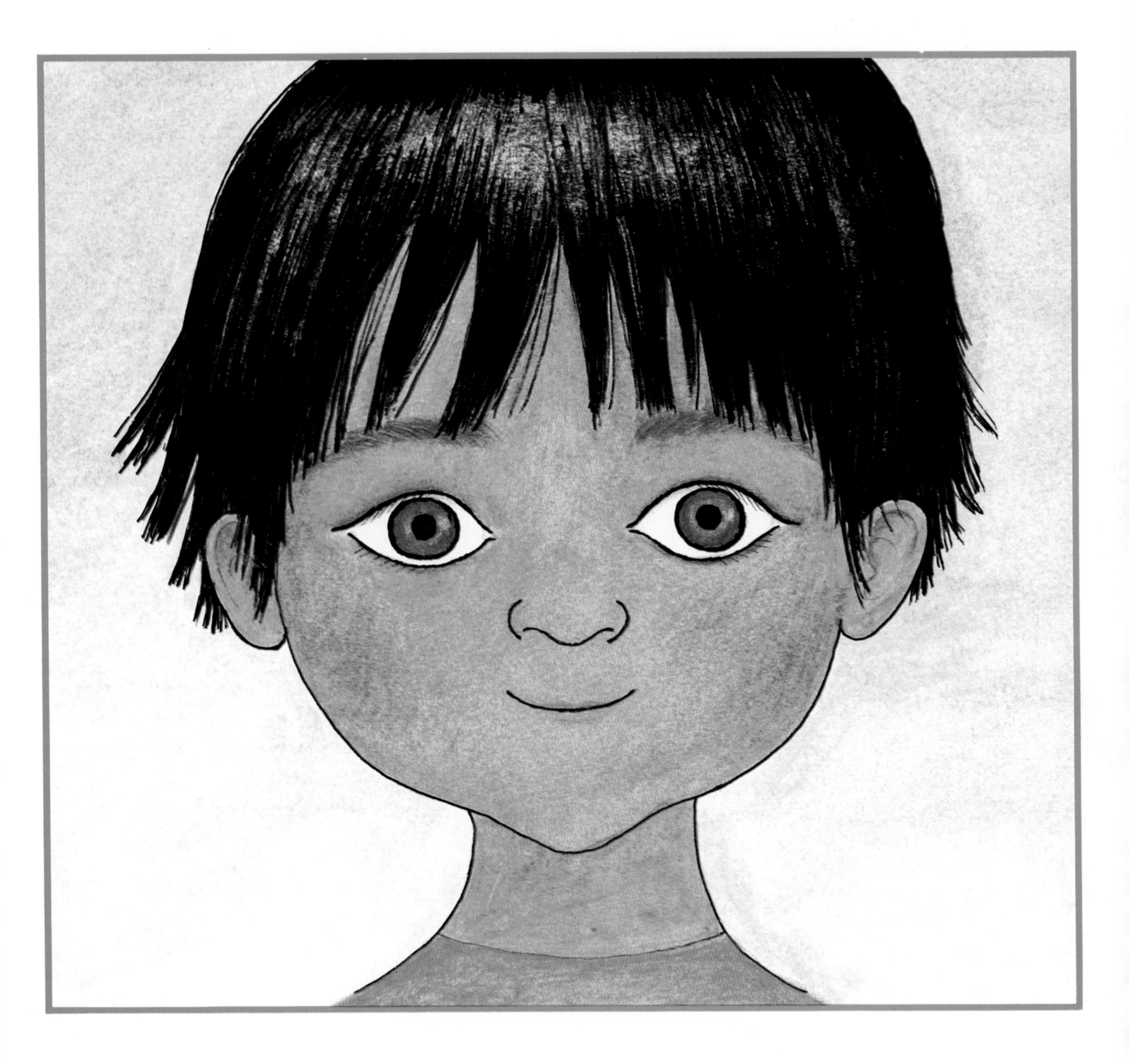

I can hear! I hear with my ears.

I can smell! I smell with my nose.

I can taste! I taste with my tongue.

I can touch! I touch with my fingers.

I do all this with my senses.
I have five senses.
When I see the sun or a frog

or my baby sister,
I use my sense of sight. I am seeing.

When I hear a drum or a fire engine
or a bird, I use my sense of hearing.
I am hearing.

When I smell soap or a pine tree or cookies
just out of the oven, I use my sense of smell.
I am smelling.

When I drink my milk and eat my food,
I use my sense of taste. I am tasting.

When I touch a kitten or a balloon or water,
I use my sense of touch. I am touching.

Sometimes I use all my senses at once.
Sometimes I use only one.
I often play a game with myself.
I guess how many senses I am using at that time.

When I look at the moon and the stars,
I use one sense. I am seeing.

When I laugh and play with my puppy,
I use four senses.
I see, hear, smell, and touch.

When I bounce a ball, I use three senses.
I see, hear, touch.

Sometimes I use more of one sense
and less of another.
But each sense is very important to me,
because it makes me aware.
To be aware is to see all there is to see . . .

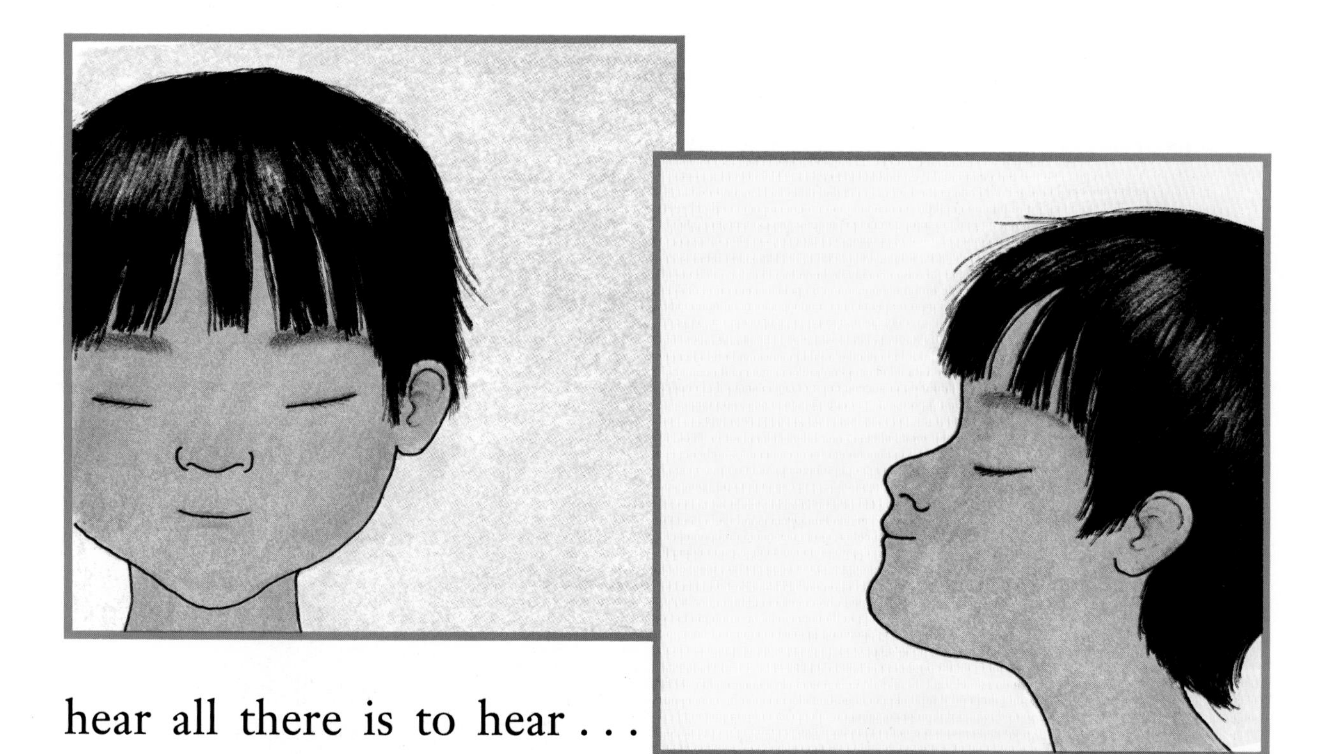

hear all there is to hear . . .

smell all there is to smell . . .

taste all there is to taste . . .

touch all there is to touch.

Wherever I go, whatever I do, every minute of the day, my senses are working.

They make me aware.

# Look All Around You

What did you learn about your senses from Aliki's book?

Think about something that interests you and that you would like to learn more about. Then find some books about your interest.

After you have read the books, tell others about what you have learned. You might want to draw some pictures to make it more interesting for your listeners.

## MEET ALIKI

Aliki uses only her first name on the books she writes and illustrates. Her whole name is Aliki Brandenberg. Her husband, Franz Brandenberg, also writes children's books, and she illustrates many of them.

Aliki at work in her garden

Aliki as a young girl

Some of Aliki's books are about imaginary people or animals. But others are about the lives of real people or about real, everyday things. Two books by Aliki that you might enjoy are *My Hands* and *Feelings*.

*by George Shannon*

*illustrated by Jose Aruego and Ariane Dewey*

Squirrel was worried.
His mother's birthday was one day away, and he still hadn't found her a present.

17
Mother's Birthday

He had looked in all the stores in town,
but nothing seemed just right.
She had perfume and books and the most
beautiful garden.

He'd already given her drawings, and songs that he'd made up.

And every time he made a cake,

he burned it.

He sighed and said, “I’ll just have to send her a plain old birthday card.”

But as he was putting the stamp on, he had an idea.

He called his mother on the telephone and said, “I’m sending you a package with a surprise inside.
Be sure to open it right away.”

The next day when the package arrived, his mother took off the ribbons and opened the box.

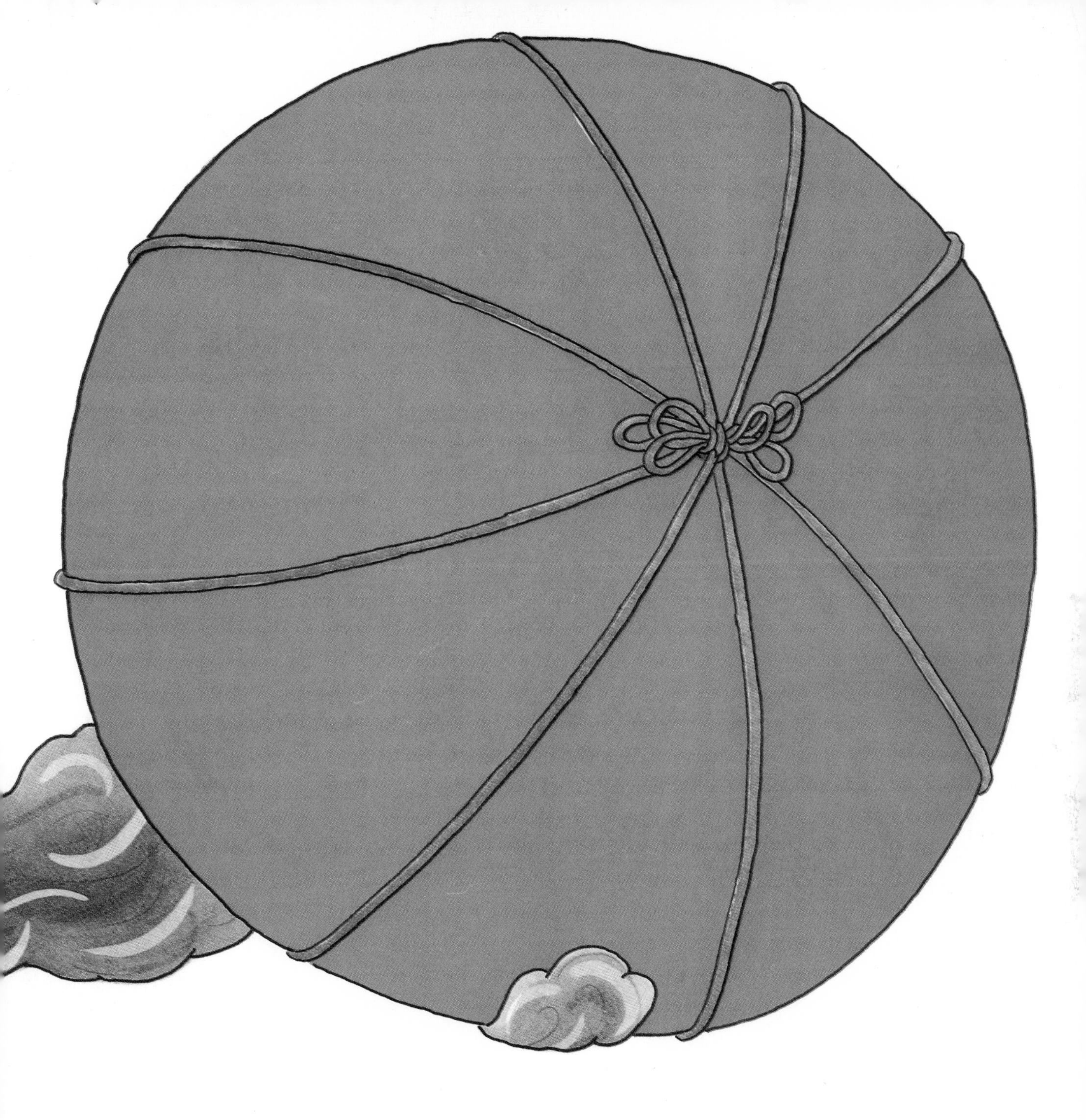

But there was only another box inside.

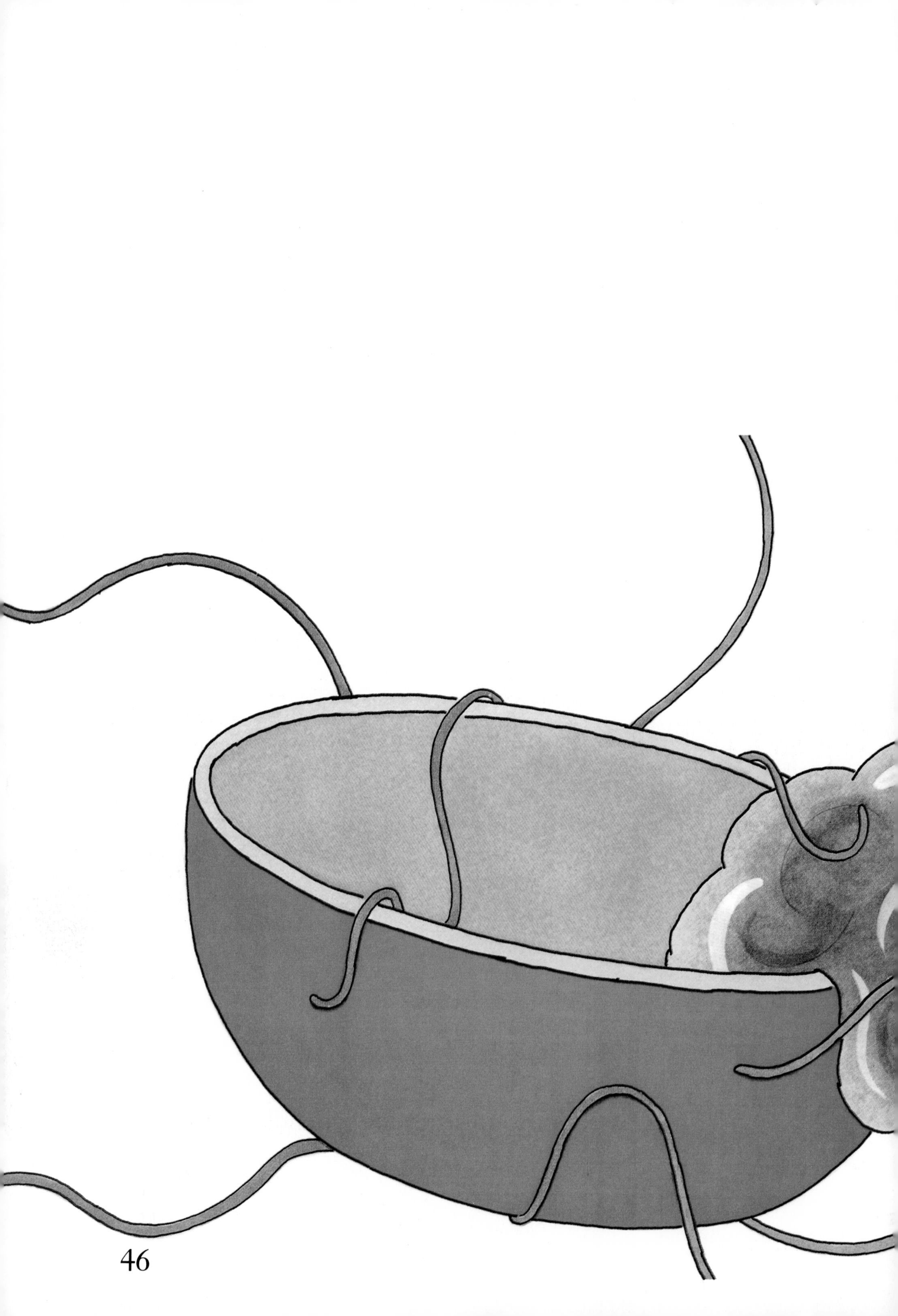

So she opened that box, and found another box.

And opened that box and found another box.

And opened that box, and found another box.

And when she opened that box . . .

Squirrel jumped out and gave her a kiss!

# Keeping Secrets

When you found out what Squirrel's surprise for his mother was, were you surprised too?

Get together with some friends to plan your own short story with a surprise ending. Be ready to tell your story to other groups. You might want to write it down and make it into a book.

# A LETTER FROM THE AUTHOR

Dear Reading Friends,

Ideas for stories are everywhere, <u>if</u> we pay attention. Ideas can come from pictures, songs, and memories. From books, too. And always from people. What they do and how they feel.

Sometimes ideas come all in order like A B C D E F G. Other times they come mixed up and incomplete like C D F E G, without an A or B. I wrote the last part of *The Surprise* first! Then I kept asking myself questions. Why do people give gifts? When? How did Squirrel get the idea for <u>this</u> gift? How would <u>I</u> feel if I were Squirrel?

I write my stories over and over and over again. I add new words, take others out, and try different ideas. I work till each story sounds to me as smooth as singing the alphabet.

Best of writing and reading wishes.

George Shannon

# MEET THE ILLUSTRATORS

Jose Aruego and Ariane Dewey worked together to make pictures for *The Surprise* and several other children's books. Jose drew the pictures, and Ariane added the color.

Jose Aruego says he grew up with many pets. His family had dogs, cats, horses, chickens, pigeons, frogs, and ducks! All the characters he draws for books are animals. He says that's because he can't draw people.

Ariane Dewey paints pictures for children's books. Ariane says she looks at colors everywhere she goes and uses many in her pictures.

## WRITING WITH PICTURES

Jose Aruego and Ariane Dewey make pictures for storybooks. Here they show you how to get started — just in case you want to write a book of your own.

Jose says that for *The Surprise*, he first drew many small pictures of squirrels to help him decide how the characters in the story would look.

Ariane says she first went to the park to look at real squirrels. This helped her decide how to color in Jose's pictures.

*by Holly Keller*

Geraldine brought her new sled down
from the attic and put her boots near the door.
"I'm ready," she said.

"It will come faster if you don't watch so much,"
Mama told her. But Geraldine wanted to watch.

"Tell me again what Papa heard on the radio," she said.
"This is the last time, Geraldine," Mama scolded.
"He heard that there is a big storm coming, and there will be at least a foot of snow."

"How much is a foot?" Geraldine asked. Mama held out her hand.
"Wow," Geraldine said, sucking in her cheeks.
"But when?"
"Soon," said Mama. "Very soon."

Geraldine put on her hat
and her jacket.
"I'm going outside to wait."
"Good," Mama said.

"Hello, Geraldine," said Mrs. Wilson, who was
coming home from the market.
"You bought a lot of apples," Geraldine said.
Mrs. Wilson nodded. "It will be hard to go
shopping when the snow comes."

Geraldine walked along with her eyes on the sky until she bumped into Mr. Peters, who was coming home from the library.

"'Afternoon, Geraldine," Mr. Peters grumbled as he picked up his books.

"I'm sorry," Geraldine said. "I was watching for the snow."

Mr. Peters cleared his throat. "Better get plenty of good books to read."

Geraldine stopped to watch Mr. Harper put seeds in his bird feeder.
"Birds get hungry in the snow," he said.

Uncle Albert was attaching the snowplow to his truck. He waved to Geraldine, and Geraldine waved back.

Geraldine started to sing. “It’s coming, it’s coming, it’s coming.” She sang all the way home and watched the sky.

But by suppertime there was still no snow, and Geraldine was weary from watching.

“Maybe it isn’t really coming,” she said. “Maybe the man on the radio is wrong. Maybe Mrs. Wilson, and Mr. Peters, and Mr. Harper, and Uncle Albert are all wrong.”

Geraldine took a last look out the window.

A star was hiding behind a cloud, and she watched it until she fell asleep.

Then in the night it came. Softly and quietly. Millions of snowflakes piled up on houses and trees. They made soft mounds on the streets and in the park, and beautiful crystals on the windows.

Geraldine heard Uncle Albert's snowplow before she opened her eyes.

"It's here!" she shouted. "It's here!"

Mrs. Wilson got right to work making apple pies.

Mr. Peters sat in front of the fireplace reading.

Mr. Harper counted eleven finches and three cardinals at his bird feeder.

And Geraldine took her sled to the top of the highest hill in the park —

and coasted all the way down.

# ANIMAL CHARACTERS

Holly Keller has created many make-believe animal characters. Like Geraldine, they also act very much as people would.

Try creating an animal character of your own. Draw a picture of it. Then give it a name and write a few sentences telling about it. You might even want to write a story about your character.

## MEET HOLLY KELLER

Holly Keller writes and draws the pictures for her books about people and animals.

The animal characters in many of Holly Keller's stories do things that real children or their families might do. Geraldine and her family are pig characters, but they talk and play just as people do.

**For each story, Holly first makes some simple drawings called sketches. She puts them together in a homemade book.**

▼

Geraldine brought her sled down from the attic and put her new boots near the kitchen door.
"I'm ready," she said.

▲

**Later, Holly uses the ideas from her sketches as she makes finished pictures.**

Mr. Peters sat in front of the fireplace reading.

**Holly Keller enjoys thinking of new story ideas.**

Two other story characters that Holly Keller writes about are Henry, an opossum who loves fireworks, and Cromwell, a rabbit who needs glasses. You might want to look for *Henry's Fourth of July* and *Cromwell's Glasses* at the library.

# Poet's Pages

Poets are authors who write poems. One very popular poet for children is Leland Jacobs.

Mr. Jacobs has written many poems. He has also put together many books of poems that were written by other poets. He says he has always loved reading and thinks that stories and poems should be read aloud often. He has made recordings of some of his own poems so that people can hear them.

Two children's poetry books edited by Mr. Jacobs are *Poems About Fur and Feather Friends* and *Funny Bone Ticklers in Verse and Rhyme*.

NO PARKING

## Bus Stop

The bus stop is a special place.
Of that there is no doubt.
A yellow line tells common cars
That they must all stay out.

The bus stop is a special spot.
Of that it's very clear.
A sign in flaming red declares
There is "NO PARKING HERE."

While other cars must cruise around
To find a parking space,
A bus must feel like royalty
To have its special place.

# The Bridge

What stands firm upon the ground?
The tall and sturdy gray bridge.

What stands ready all year round?
The faithful night-and-day bridge.

What stands reaching toward the sun?
The mighty, towering, strong bridge.

What stands welcoming everyone?
The busy-all-day-long bridge.

What stands safe from waters blue?
The reaching-for-the-sky bridge.

What stands waiting just for you?
The quick-cross-over high bridge.

## The Subway Train

The subway train, the subway train,
If you'll permit me to explain,
Is like a busy beetle black
That scoots along a silver track;
And, whether it be night or day,
The beetle has to light its way,
Because the only place it's found
Is deep, deep, deep,
deep, underground.

# BOOKS BY FAVORITE AUTHORS

**The Great Sea Monster**
*by Berthe Amoss*
This author tells you how she creates a book about a sea monster. Then she shows you how *you* can write a book.

**At Mary Bloom's**
*by Aliki*
Mary Bloom has a house full of animals. But she is always ready for more!

**My Visit to the Dinosaurs** *by Aliki*

Dinosaurs were amazing animals. Come along on a trip to a museum to look at dinosaur skeletons.

**Lizzie's Invitation**

*by Holly Keller*

It seems that everyone has an invitation to the party — except Lizzie.

**Dance Away**

*by George Shannon*

Rabbit's friends are trapped by a hungry fox and are too scared to move. Rabbit gets them moving in no time!

# Old Favorites

# BOOK 2

Did you know that many of the rhymes, stories, and songs that you know are the same ones that your parents, grandparents, and even your great-grandparents enjoyed when they were your age?

Through the years these old stories, rhymes, and songs have been retold and reread over and over again because they're everybody's favorites.

# Contents

# The Counting Song

*retold and illustrated by Robin Michal Koontz*

This old man,
he played one,
He played knick-knack
on my drum,
With a knick-knack,
paddy whack,
give the dog a bone,
This old man
came rolling home.

This old man,
he played two,
He played knick-knack
on my shoe,
With a knick-knack,
paddy whack,
give the dog a bone,
This old man
came rolling home.

This old man,
he played three,
He played knick-knack
on my knee,
With a knick-knack,
paddy whack,
give the dog a bone,
This old man
came rolling home.

3
3

This old man,
he played four,
He played knick-knack
on my door,
With a knick-knack,
paddy whack,
give the dog a bone,
This old man
came rolling home.

This old man,
he played five,
He played knick-knack
on my hive,
With a knick-knack,
paddy whack,
give the dog a bone,
This old man
came rolling home.

This old man,
he played six,
He played knick-knack
on my sticks,
With a knick-knack,
paddy whack,
give the dog a bone,
This old man
came rolling home.

This old man,
he played seven,
He played knick-knack
up to heaven,
With a knick-knack,
paddy whack,
give the dog a bone,
This old man
came rolling home.

This old man,
he played eight,
He played knick-knack
at the gate,
With a knick-knack,
paddy whack,
give the dog a bone,
This old man
came rolling home.

This old man,
he played nine,
He played knick-knack
on my line,
With a knick-knack,
paddy whack,
give the dog a bone,
This old man
came rolling home.

This old man,
he played ten,
He played knick-knack
over again,
With a knick-knack,
paddy whack,
give the dog a bone,
This old man
came rolling home.

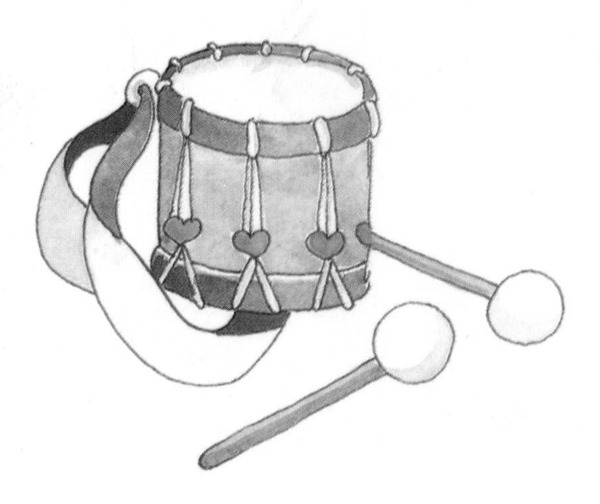

# Rhyme Time

There are many rhymes for number words in *This Old Man.*

Think of other number rhymes that would work in this old song. Make a list of your rhyming word pairs and sing your new song with some friends.

# THIS OLD MAN

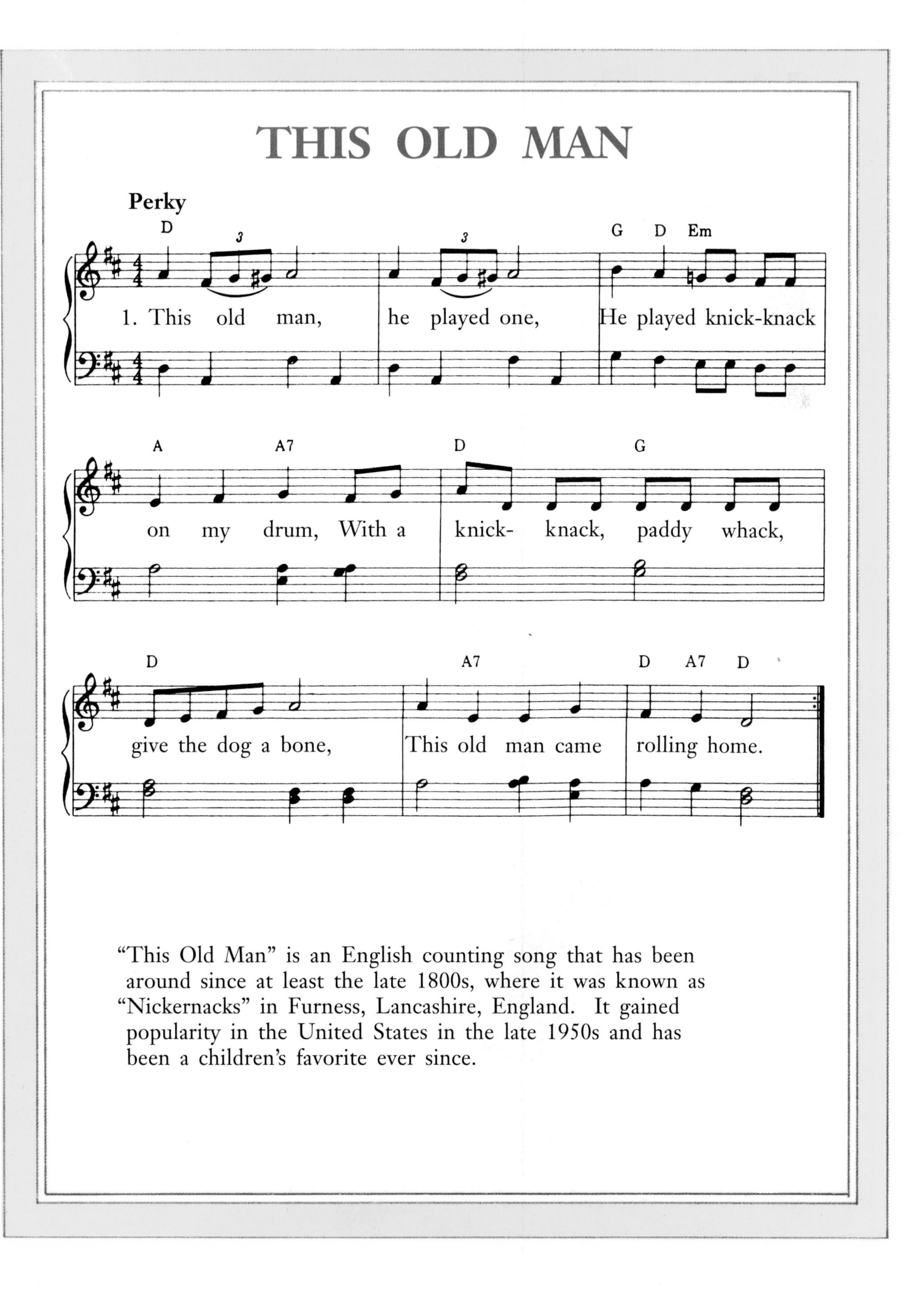


"This Old Man" is an English counting song that has been around since at least the late 1800s, where it was known as "Nickernacks" in Furness, Lancashire, England. It gained popularity in the United States in the late 1950s and has been a children's favorite ever since.

# Meet the Author and Illustrator

Art has been a part of Robin Michal Koontz's life since she was a child. She is the daughter of an artist, Virginia Koontz.

Besides illustrating children's books, Robin Michal Koontz owns a business. She makes gift tags and greeting cards.

Ms. Koontz lives with her husband, two cats, and a dog. She says that their two cats gave her ideas for her first Mother Goose rhyme book about cats called *Pussycat Ate the Dumplings.*

## The Dog and His Shadow

*an Aesop's fable as told and illustrated by Tomie dePaola*

Once a dog was given a nice bone. He put it in his mouth and set off for home. As he was crossing the bridge over a river he looked down and saw his reflection in the water. "Why, there is a dog looking up at me," he said, "and he has a bone too! But his bone is bigger than mine. I'll just drop this smaller bone and grab that bigger bone away."

At that, the dog dropped the bone and jumped into the river, losing the bone for good — and getting very wet as well!

*Moral: It's better to be content with what you already have instead of chasing after what's not there.*

# STONE

*retold by Ann McGovern*

# SOUP

*illustrated by Cat Bowman Smith*

A young man was walking.
He walked and he walked.
He walked all night.
And he walked all day.

He was tired. And he was hungry.

At last he came to a big house.
"What a fine house," he said.
"There will be plenty of food
for me here."

He knocked on the door.
A little old lady opened it.

"Good lady," said the young man,
"I am very hungry.
Can you give me something to eat?"

"I have nothing to give you,"
said the little old lady.
"I have nothing in the house.
I have nothing in the garden."
And she began to close the door.

"Stop," said the young man.
"If you will not give me
something to eat,
will you give me a stone?"

"A stone?" said the little old lady.
"What will you do with a stone?
You cannot eat a stone!"

"Ah," said the young man.
"I can make soup from a stone."

Now the little old lady had
never heard of that.
Make soup from a stone?
Fancy that.

"There are stones in the road,"
said the little old lady.

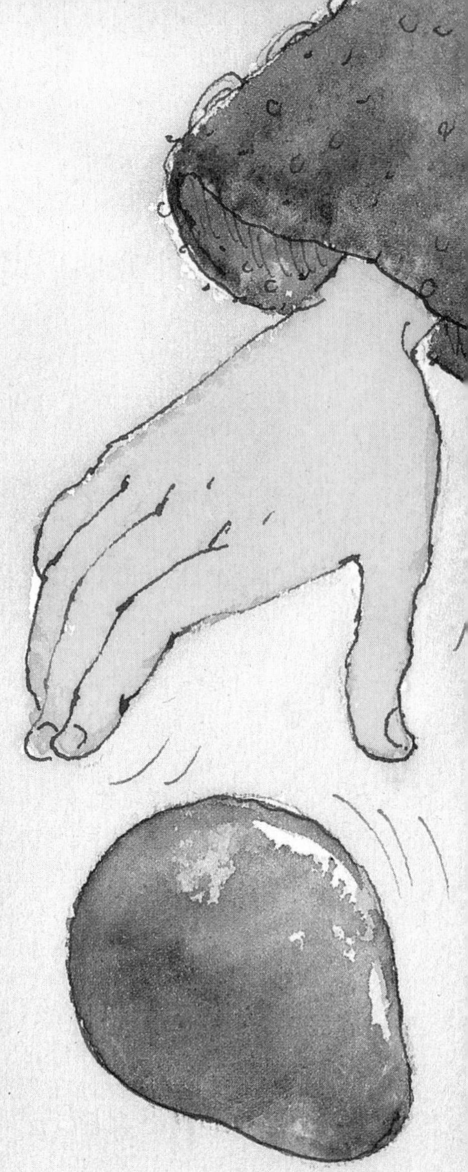

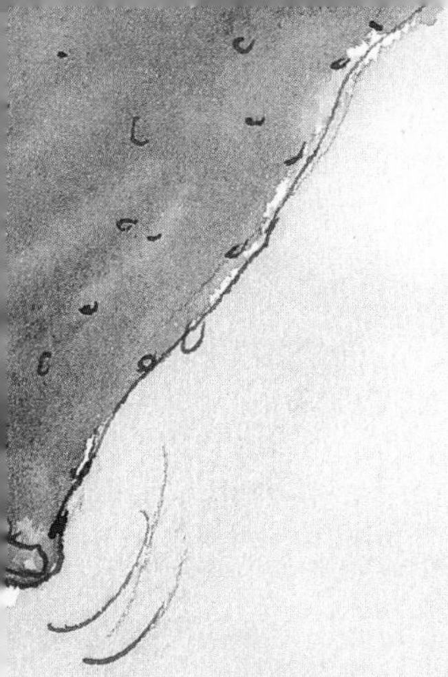

The young man picked up a round,
gray stone.
"This stone will make wonderful soup,"
he said.
"Now get me a pot."

The little old lady got a pot.

"Fill the pot with water
and put it on the fire,"
the young man said.

The little old lady did as she was told.
And soon the water was bubbling
in the pot.

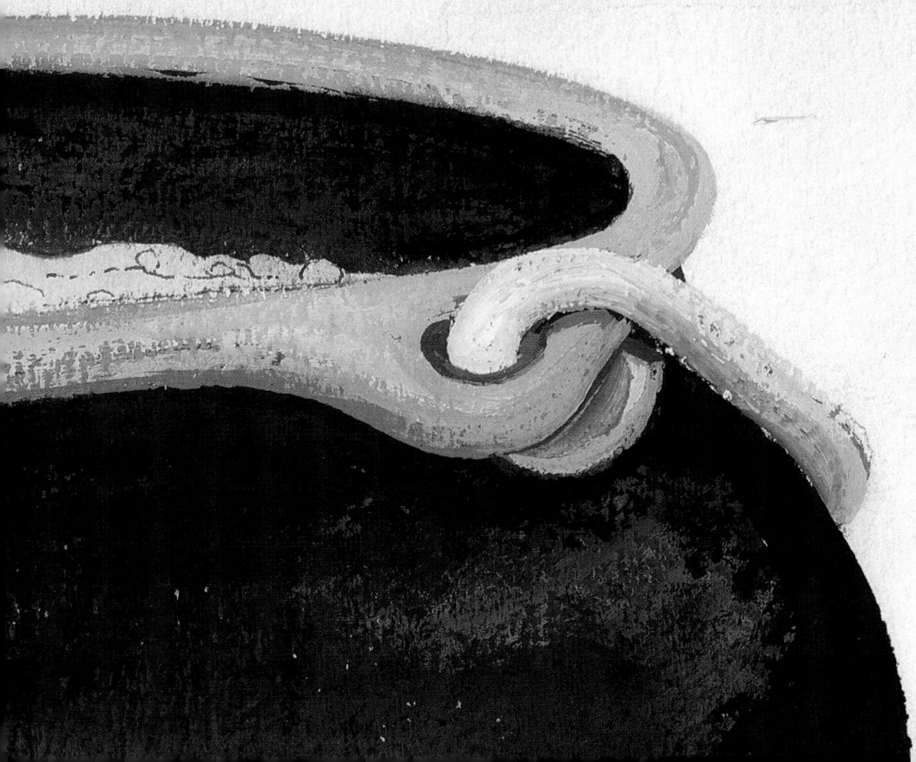

The young man put the round,
gray stone into the pot.
"Now we will wait for the stone to
cook into soup," he said.

The pot bubbled and bubbled.

After a while, the little old lady said,
"This soup is cooking fast."

"It is cooking fast now,"
said the hungry young man.
"But it would cook faster with
some onions."

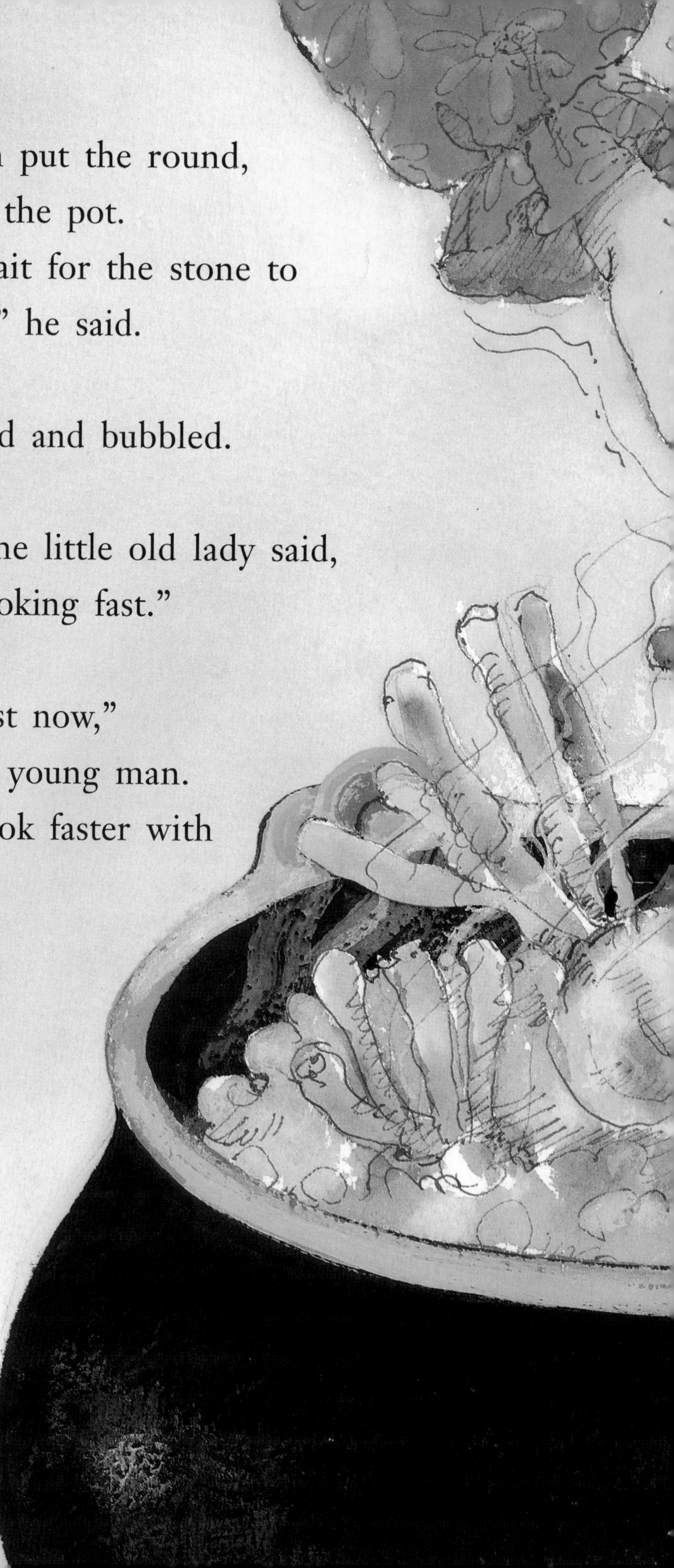

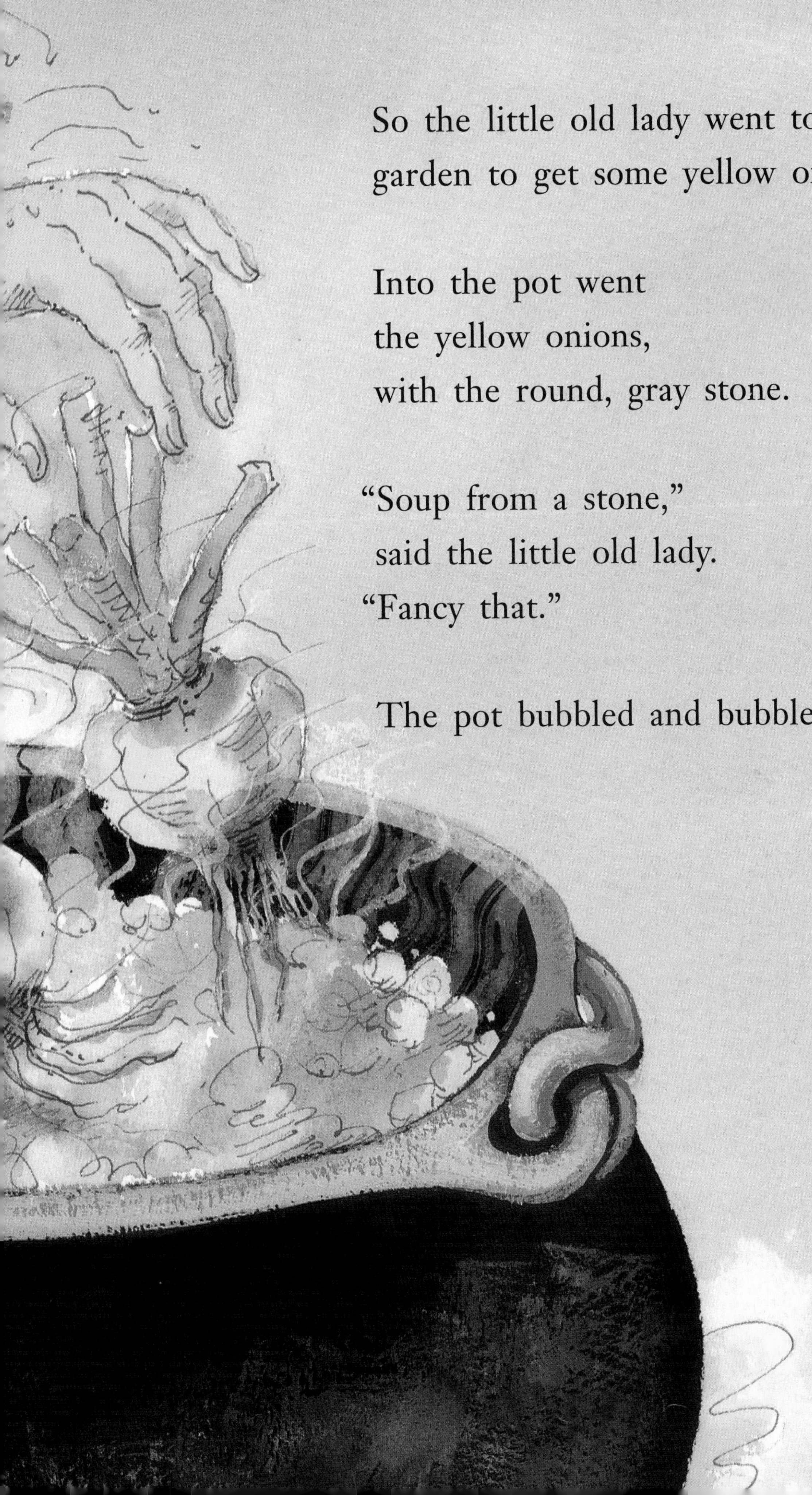

So the little old lady went to the garden to get some yellow onions.

Into the pot went
the yellow onions,
with the round, gray stone.

"Soup from a stone,"
said the little old lady.
"Fancy that."

The pot bubbled and bubbled.

After a while, the little old lady said,
"This soup smells good."

"It smells good now,"
said the hungry young man.
"But it would smell better
with some carrots."

So the little old lady
went out to the garden
and pulled up all the carrots
she could carry.

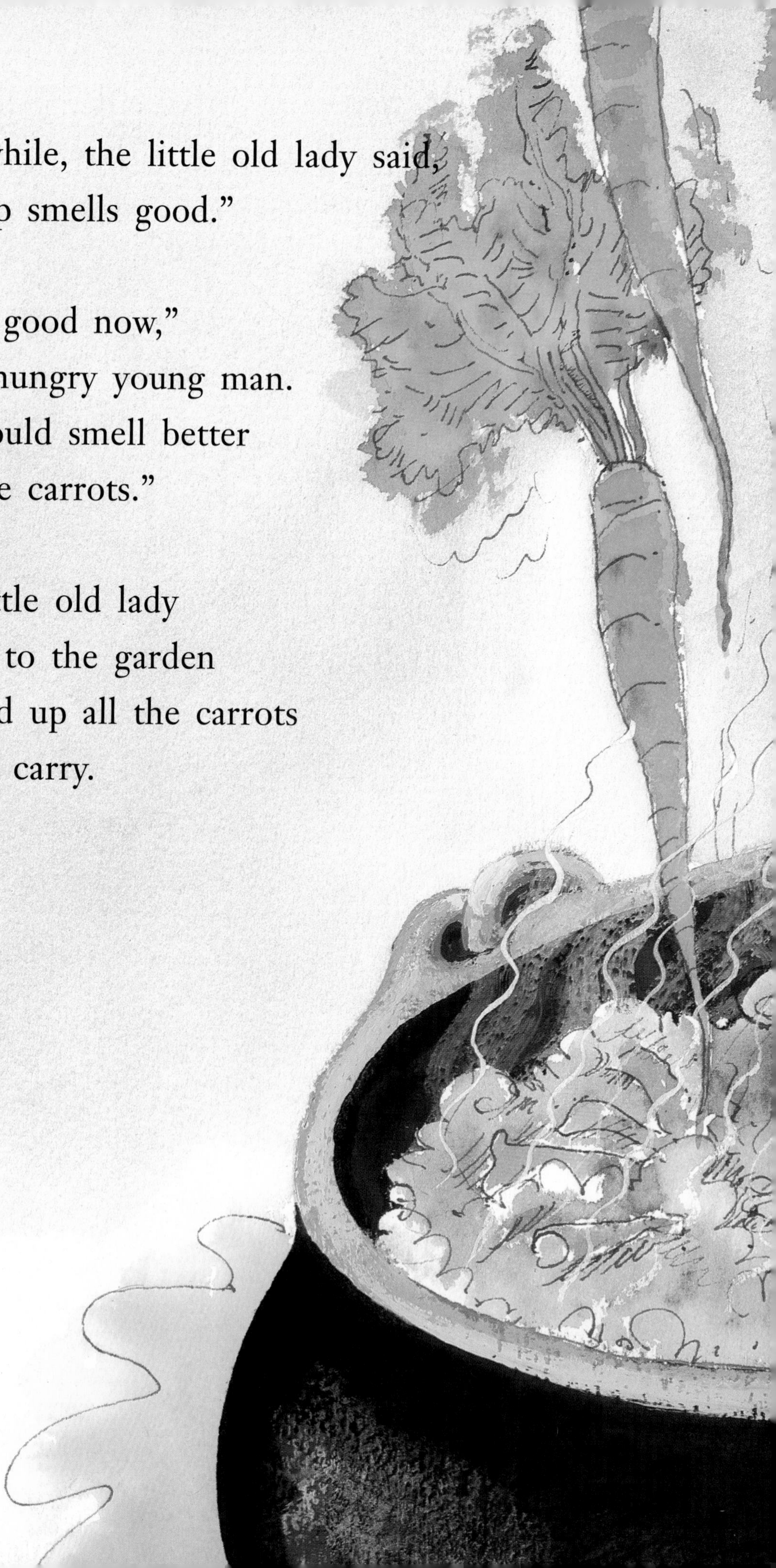

Into the pot went
the long, thin carrots,
with the yellow onions,
and the round, gray stone.

"Soup from a stone,"
said the little old lady.
"Fancy that."

The pot bubbled and bubbled.

After a while, the little old lady said,
"This soup tastes good."

"It tastes good now,"
said the hungry young man.
"But it would taste better
with beef bones."

So the little old lady went to get
some juicy beef bones.

Into the pot went
the juicy beef bones,
and the long, thin carrots,
and the yellow onions,
and the round, gray stone.

"Soup from a stone,"
said the little old lady.
"Fancy that."

The pot bubbled and bubbled.

After a while, the little old lady said,
"This soup is fit for a prince."

"It is fit for a prince now,"
said the hungry young man.
"But it would be fit for a king
with a bit of pepper
and a handful of salt."

So the little old lady
got the pepper and the salt.

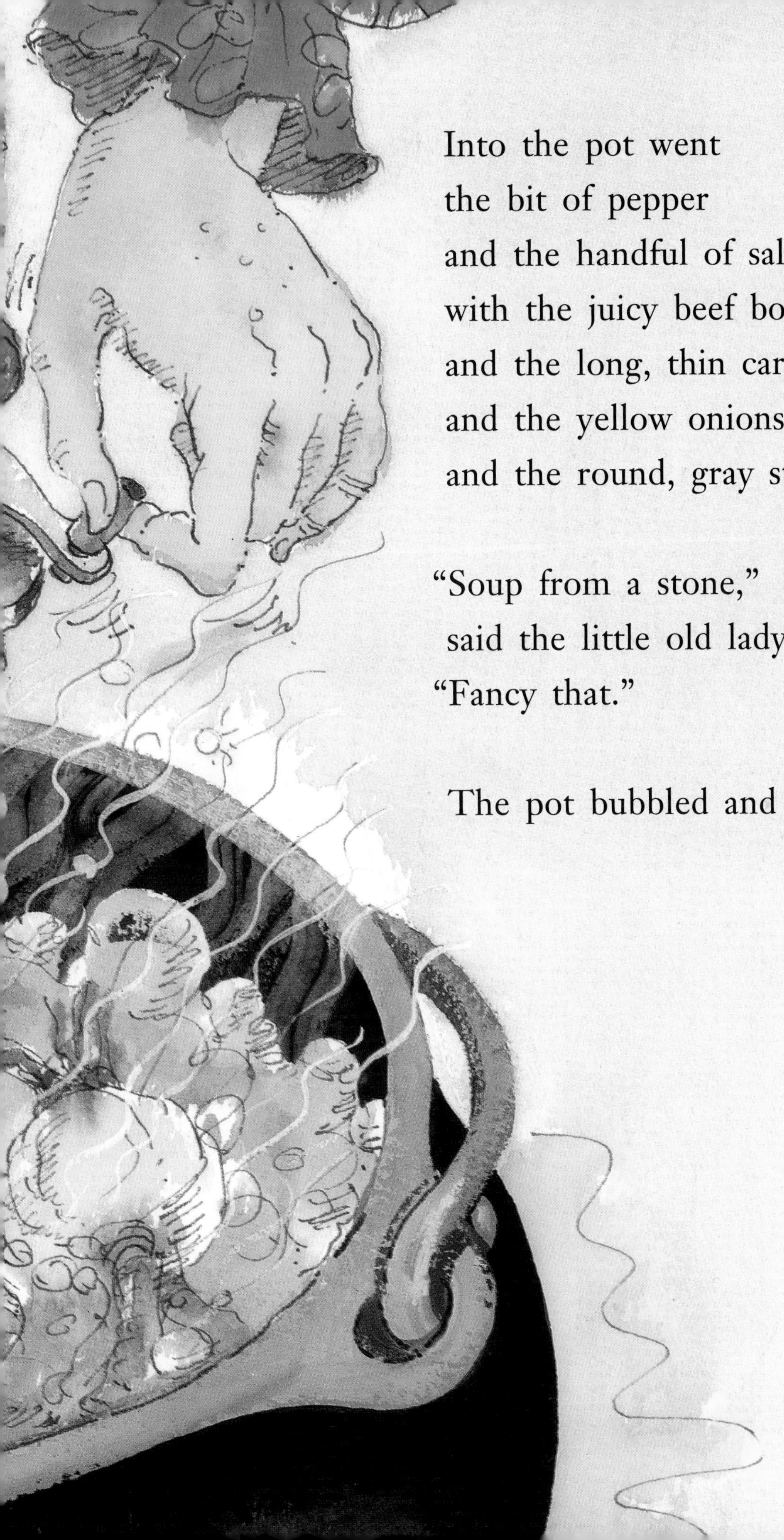

Into the pot went
the bit of pepper
and the handful of salt,
with the juicy beef bones,
and the long, thin carrots,
and the yellow onions,
and the round, gray stone.

"Soup from a stone,"
said the little old lady.
"Fancy that."

The pot bubbled and bubbled.

After a while, the little old lady said,
"This soup is too thin."

"It is too thin now,"
said the hungry young man.
"But it would be nice and thick
with some butter and barley."

So the little old lady
went to get butter and barley.

Into the pot went
the butter and barley,
with the bit of pepper
and the handful of salt,
and the juicy beef bones,
and the long, thin carrots,
and the yellow onions,
and the round, gray stone.

"Soup from a stone,"
said the little old lady.
"Fancy that."

The pot bubbled and bubbled.

After a while, the little old lady
tasted the soup again.
"That is good soup," she said.

"Yes," said the hungry young man.
"This soup is fit for a king.
Now we will eat it."

"Stop!" said the little old lady.
"This soup is indeed fit for a king.
Now I will set a table fit for a king."

So she took out her best
tablecloth and her best dishes.

Then the little old lady
and the hungry young man
ate all the soup —

the soup made with
the butter and barley,
and the bit of pepper,
and the handful of salt,
and the juicy beef bones,
and the long, thin carrots,
and the yellow onions,
and the round, gray stone.

"Soup from a stone,"
said the little old lady.
"Fancy that."

"Now I must be on my way,"
said the young man.
He took the stone out of the pot,
and put it into his pocket.

"Why are you taking the stone?"
said the little old lady.

"Well," said the young man.
"The stone is not cooked enough.
I will have to cook it some more
tomorrow."

And the young man said
good-bye.

He walked on down the road.
He walked and he walked.
"What a fine supper
I will have tomorrow,"
he said to himself.

"Soup from a stone.
Fancy that."

# A Fine Supper For Tomorrow

Where do you think the young man might go next? Do you think he will find someone else who will help him make stone soup? Why?

With a friend, write a story that tells where you think the young man might go and what he might do. Draw a picture to help you tell your story.

# Meet the Author

Ann McGovern writes many different kinds of books for children. She writes stories about famous people such as Christopher Columbus and Harriet Tubman. She writes about sharks, different kinds of sea life, and other science stories. She also writes new versions of old folktales, such as *Stone Soup*.

# Meet the Illustrator

Cat Bowman Smith has had many different jobs as an illustrator. She began her work with a newspaper in New York. Later, she started drawing pictures for *Cricket,* a magazine for children. She has also illustrated several books for children, including *Princess Bee and the Royal Good-Night Story* by Sandy Asher.

Cat lives in Rochester, New York, with her husband. They have four grown children.

## Old Man Daisy

Old Man Daisy,
You're driving me crazy,
Up the ladder, down the ladder,
One, two, three.
Pepper, salt, vinegar,
H,O,T!

## A Sailor Went to Sea

A sailor went to sea, sea, sea,
To see what he could see, see, see,
But all that he could see, see, see,
Was the bottom of the deep blue
sea, sea, sea!

## Miss Lucy

Miss Lucy had a baby,
His name was Tiny Tim.
She put him in the bathtub
To teach him how to swim.

He drank up all the water,
He ate the bar of soap,
He tried to eat the bathtub
But it wouldn't go down his throat!

Miss Lucy called the doctor,
Miss Lucy called the nurse,
Miss Lucy called the lady
With the alligator purse.

"Mumps," said the doctor.
"Measles," said the nurse.
"Hiccups," said the lady
With the alligator purse.

# The Three Little Pigs

*retold and illustrated*

*by Paul Galdone*

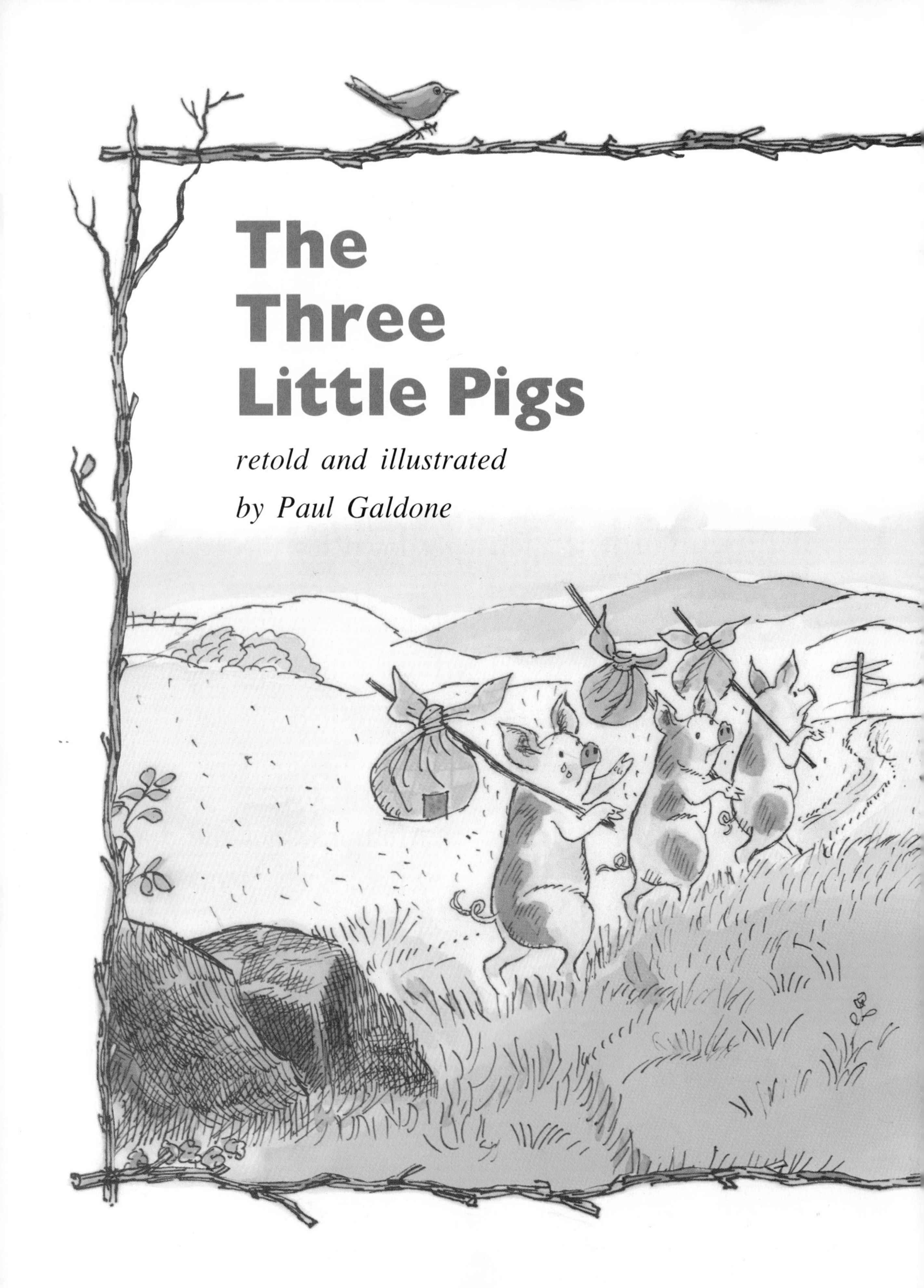

Once upon a time, there was an old sow with three little pigs. She had no money to keep them, so she sent them off to seek their fortune.

The first little pig met a man
with a bundle of straw,
and said to him:
"Please, man, give me that straw
to build me a house."

So the man did,
and the little pig
built his house with it.

Along came a wolf.
He knocked at the door, and said:
"Little pig, little pig, let me come in."

"No, no," said the little pig.
"Not by the hair of my
chinny chin chin."

"Then I'll huff, and I'll puff,
and I'll blow your house in,"
said the wolf.

So the wolf huffed, and he puffed,
and he blew the house in.
And he ate up the first little pig.

The second little pig met a man
with a bundle of sticks, and said:
"Please, man, give me those sticks
to build me a house."

So the man did,
and the little pig built
his house with them.

Then along came the wolf, and said:
"Little pig, little pig,
let me come in."

"No, no! Not by the hair
of my chinny chin chin."

"Then I'll huff, and I'll puff,
and I'll blow your house in,"
said the wolf.

So he huffed, and he puffed,
and he huffed and he puffed, and
at last he blew the house in.
And he ate up the second little pig.

The third little pig met a man
with a load of bricks, and said:
"Please, man, give me those bricks
to build me a house."

So the man did,
and the little pig built
his house with them.

Soon the same wolf
came along, and said:
"Little pig, little pig,
let me come in."

"No, no! Not by the hair
of my chinny chin chin."

"Then I'll huff, and I'll puff,
and I'll blow your house in,"
said the wolf.

Well, he huffed, and he puffed
and he huffed and he puffed
and he huffed and he puffed.

But he could *not* blow the house in.

At last the wolf stopped
huffing and puffing, and said:
"Little pig, I know where there is
a nice field of turnips."

"Where?" said the little pig.

"On Mr. Smith's farm," said the wolf.
"I will come for you tomorrow morning.
We will go together,
and get some turnips for dinner."

"Very well," said the little pig.
"What time will you come?"

"Oh, at six o'clock,"
said the wolf.

Well, the little pig got up at five.
He went to Mr. Smith's farm,
and got the turnips
before the wolf came to his house.

"Little pig, are you ready?"
asked the wolf.
The little pig said, "Ready!
I have been and come back again
and I got a nice potful of turnips
for my dinner."

The wolf was very angry.
But then he thought of
another way to get
the little pig, so he said:
"Little pig,
I know where there
is a nice apple tree."

"Where?" said the pig.

"Down at Merry Garden,"
replied the wolf.
"I will come for you
at five o'clock tomorrow morning
and we will get some apples."

Well, the little pig got up
the next morning at four o'clock,
and went off for the apples.
He wanted to get back home
before the wolf came. But it was a
long way to Merry Garden,
and then he had to climb the tree.
Just as he was climbing back down
with his basket full of apples,
he saw the wolf coming!

"Little pig!" the wolf said.
"You got here before me!
Are the apples nice?"

"Yes, very," said the little pig.
"I will throw one down to you."
And he threw the apple as far
as he could throw.
While the wolf ran to pick it up,
the little pig jumped down and ran home.

The next day the wolf came again
and said to the little pig:
"Little pig, there is a fair at Shanklin
this afternoon. Would you like to go?"

"Oh, yes," said the little pig.
"When will you come to get me?"

"At three," said the wolf.

Well, the little pig went off at two o'clock
and bought a butter churn at the fair.

He was going home with it
when he saw the wolf coming!

The little pig jumped into the butter churn
to hide.

The churn fell over and rolled
down the hill with the little pig in it.
This frightened the wolf so much
that he turned around and ran home.

Later the wolf went to the little pig's house
and told him what had happened.

"A great round thing came rolling down the hill right at me," the wolf said.

"Hah, I frightened you then," said the little pig.

"I went to the fair and bought a butter churn. When I saw you, I got into it, and rolled down the hill."

The wolf was very angry indeed.
"I'm going to climb down your chimney
and eat you up!" he said.

When the little pig heard the wolf on the roof ~

he hung a pot
full of water in the fireplace.
Then he built a blazing fire.
Just as the wolf was coming down the chimney,
the little pig took the cover off the pot,
and in fell the wolf.
The little pig quickly put on the cover again,
boiled up the wolf, and ate him for supper.

And the little pig lived happily ever afterward.

# Let's do it again!

With a group of friends, act out the story of *The Three Little Pigs.* Use your own words and actions to retell the story. Be sure to make your voice sound like the voice of a pig or a wolf.

Perform your play with your friends.

# Meet the Author and Illustrator

Before Paul Galdone became an author, he worked for a book publishing company. His job was to draw the pictures for other people's books. He soon decided that he would much rather draw pictures for his *own* books!

Mr. Galdone especially liked to retell and illustrate favorite old tales such as *The Three Little Pigs* and *The Three Billy Goats Gruff.* He also illustrated nursery rhymes and songs.

Can you imagine writing and illustrating almost two hundred books? Paul Galdone enjoyed making picture books so much that he did just that!

**The Old Woman Who Lived In A Shoe**

There was an old woman
Who lived in a shoe.
She had so many children
She didn't know what to do!

*~ anonymous*

**The Old Woman**

You know the old woman
Who lived in a shoe?
And had so many children
She didn't know what to do?

I think if she lived in
A little shoe-house ~
That little old woman was
Surely a mouse!

*by Beatrix Potter*

# More Old Favorites

**The Princess and the Pea**
*a Hans Christian Andersen tale*
*illustrated by Eve Tharlet*

To find out how to tell if someone is a real princess, just read this old fairy tale.

**Each Peach Pear Plum: An I-Spy Story**
*by Janet and Allan Ahlberg*

Can you find Tom Thumb, or Jack and Jill, or other story friends in this book? Use your eye to play "I spy."

**Little Tuppen**

*retold and illustrated by Paul Galdone*

Cluck-cluck! A hen rushes off to get water for her chick. But first she must find a cup to put it in.

**Old MacDonald Had a Farm**

*retold and illustrated by Carol Jones*

Here's a new version of an old favorite play party song. You can peek to find the next animals in line to play the game.

# BOOK 3

# PROBLEMS, PROBLEMS!

Problems, problems!
Some problems may seem big,
and others may seem small.
Here are some stories and poems
about all kinds of problems!

CONTENTS

SHARED READING

# JIMMY LEE DID IT

by Pat Cummings

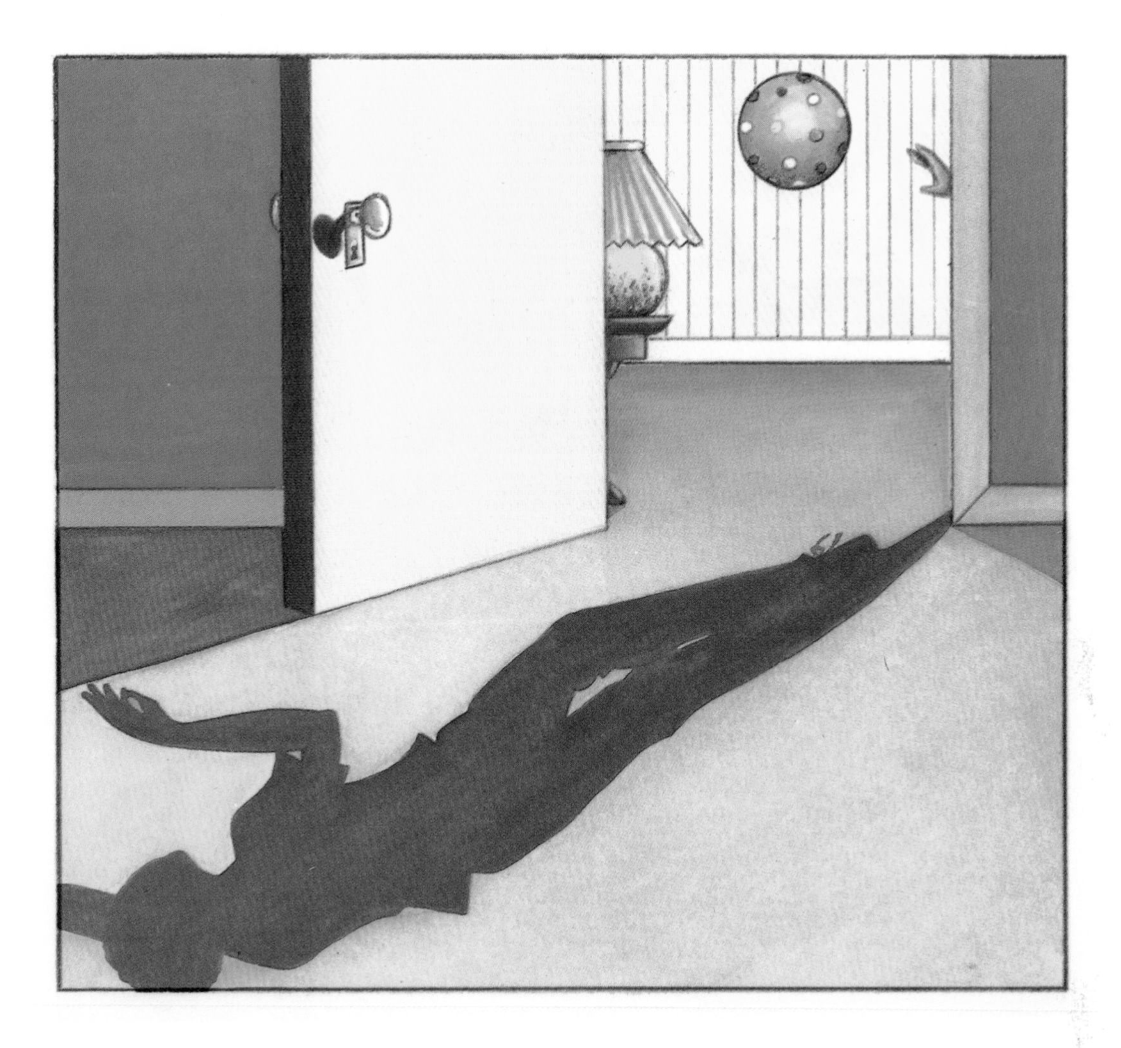

Jimmy Lee is back again
And nothing is the same.
He's causing lots of trouble,
While my brother takes the blame.

Artie made his bed, he said.
But Jimmy thinks he's smart.
While Artie read his comics,
Jimmy pulled the sheets apart.

Dad fixed us pancakes
And Artie said his tasted fine,
But Jimmy Lee had just been there
And eaten most of mine.

I heard the crash of breaking glass,
But turned too late, I guess.
"Jimmy Lee did it," Artie said,
As we cleaned up the mess.

When Artie's room got painted,
Jimmy Lee was in the hall.
He used up Artie's crayons
Drawing pictures on the wall.

And when I finally found my bear,
I asked Artie, "Who hid it?"
He told me frankly, "Angel,
It was Jimmy Lee who did it."

He caused so much trouble
That I began to see —
The only way to stop it
Was to capture Jimmy Lee.

I knew about his sweet tooth,
So I set a tasty trap,
But Jimmy Lee just waited
Till I had to take my nap.

I spread out all my marbles
To trip up Jimmy Lee.
The dog slid by and scratched the floor
And Mom got mad at me.

I hid in the hall closet
And I never made a sound,
But Jimmy Lee will only come
When Artie is around.

I don't know what he looks like,
He never leaves a trace —
Except for spills and tears
And Artie's things about the place.

Since Artie won't describe him,
He remains a mystery.
But if you're smart, you'll listen
And watch out for Jimmy Lee.

## Jimmy Lee —
# The Mystery

Help Angel solve the
mystery of Jimmy Lee!
Write her a letter.
Tell her who **you** think
Jimmy Lee might be.
Be sure to tell Angel
how you figured it out.

# Poems About Everyday Problems

## Whistling

Oh, I can laugh and I can sing
and I can scream and shout,
but when I try to whistle,
the whistle won't come out.

I shape my lips the proper way,
I make them small and round,
but when I blow, just air comes out,
there is no whistling sound.

But I'll keep trying very hard
to whistle loud and clear,
and some day soon I'll whistle tunes
for everyone to hear.

*by Jack Prelutsky*

## A Problem

My zipper is stuck
    And what shall I do?
Give it a jerk
    And break it in two,
Give it a tug
    And then it will jam —
I think I'll just sit here
    The way that I am.

*by Marchette Chute*

## I Eat My Peas with Honey

I eat my peas with honey;
I've done it all my life.
It makes the peas taste funny,
But it keeps them on the knife.

*—Anonymous*

## Shoe Laces

Although I've tried and tried and tried,
I cannot keep my laces tied.
I really don't know what to do —

Unless I stick them tied with glue —
Except that such a sticky mess
Would not be good for shoes, I guess.

*by Leland Jacobs*

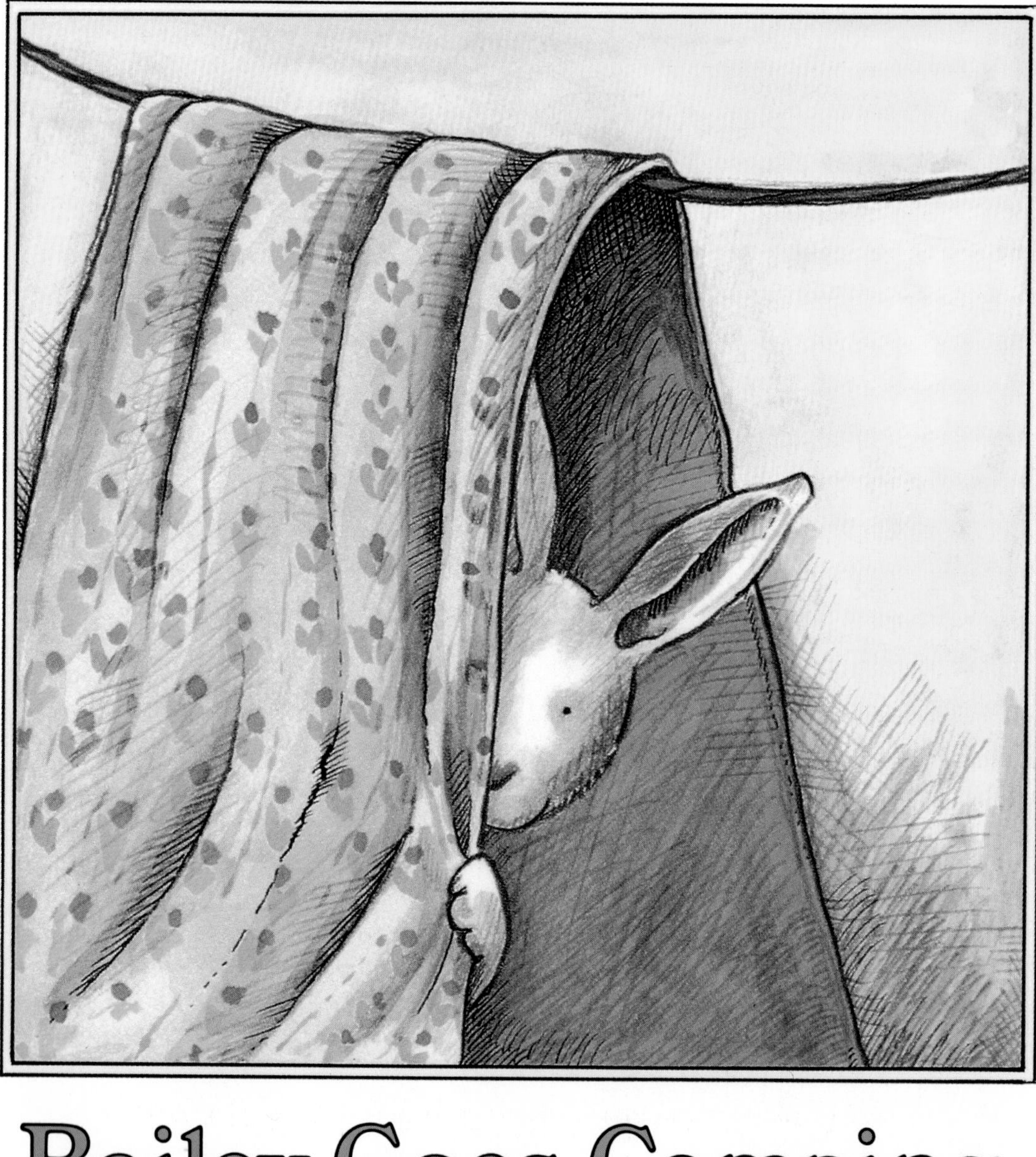

# Bailey Goes Camping

by Kevin Henkes

Bruce and Betty were Bunny Scouts.
They were going camping.
Bailey had to stay home.
"I want to go camping," said Bailey.

"You're too little to go," said Bruce.
"But in a few years you can,"
said Betty.
"Don't feel bad, Bailey," said Bruce.
"It's not *that* great. All we do is eat
hot dogs and live in a tent and go

swimming and fishing and hunt for bears and tell ghost stories and fall asleep under the stars."

"And don't forget roasting marshmallows," said Betty. "That's best of all!"

Bailey watched Bruce and Betty leave.
"It's not fair," he said.

"Come on," said Papa, "let's play baseball."
"No," said Bailey.
"Want to help me bake cookies?" said Mama.
"No," said Bailey.
"We could read a book," said Papa.
"No," said Bailey. "I want to go camping."

"You're too little to go," said Papa.
"But in a few years you can," said Mama.
"Don't feel bad, Bailey," said Papa. "It's not *that* great."
"Oh, yes, it is," said Bailey. "You get to eat hot dogs and live in a tent and go swimming and fishing and hunt for bears and tell ghost stories and fall asleep under the stars. And best of all, you roast marshmallows."

"You know," said Mama, "you can do all those things right here."

"I *can*?" said Bailey.

"He *can*?" said Papa.

"Yes," said Mama, smiling.

That afternoon,
Bailey ate hot dogs

and lived in a tent.

He went swimming

and fishing.

That night, Bailey went
on a bear hunt

and told ghost stories.

And best of all,
he roasted marshmallows —

before falling asleep under the stars.

# Let's Camp In

Bailey couldn't camp out with his brother and sister so he pretended to go camping right in his own home. You can pretend to go camping too — right in your classroom.

Get together with four or five friends to plan a classroom camp. Decide what things in the classroom you might use as props for your camp-in.

1.
SWEET SOLUTIONS
AT THE 1904 WORLD'S FAIR IN ST. LOUIS, MISSOURI, ICE CREAM CONES WERE INVENTED. DID YOU KNOW THAT THE ICE CREAM CONE WAS A SWEET SOLUTION TO A PROBLEM?
1904 WORLD'S FAIR

2.
I DON'T HAVE ANY MORE DISHES. HOW WILL I SELL MY ICE CREAM?
ICE CREAM

5.
WAFFLES

6.
WAFFLES
ICE CREAM

3.
I WISH PEOPLE WOULD BUY MORE OF MY WAFFLES.
WAFFLES

4.
HMMM...
WAFFLES
ICE CREAM

7.
TRY SOME NEW ICE CREAM CONES!

# Anna's Secret Friend

**by Yoriko Tsutsui**
illustrated by Akiko Hayashi

Anna was excited about moving to a new house in a new town. She was especially pleased to be living close to the mountains. But already she was missing the friends she had left behind.

Still, there was hardly time to think about anything because there were so many boxes to be carried into the new house.

Soon every room was full of boxes.
Anna began to help unpack, but before long she was bored and tired.

Suddenly she heard a quiet tip tap sound. The noise came from the front door.

"I heard the postman," said Anna.
"I don't think it could have been," said her mother.
"We haven't told anyone our new address yet," said her father.
"But I *did* hear someone," said Anna, and she went to look.

At the front door Anna saw that her mother and her father were right. There were no letters, but there was something much nicer — a small bunch of violets that lay on the floor. How did the pretty flowers get there?

Quickly Anna opened the front door to see who could have brought the flowers. But all she could see was an unfamiliar street, and lots of people she hadn't seen before walking by.

Next morning Anna's mother did more unpacking. "I just don't know who could have given those violets to us yesterday," she said to Anna.

Just then, Anna heard that noise again — a quiet tip tap sound at the front door.

Anna ran to the front door. This time there were three dandelions in the letter box. Anna carefully picked out the yellow flowers and opened the front door. But once again all she saw were people she didn't know walking along the street.

The next day Anna went shopping with her mother. It was very strange to be going into new shops and seeing people she didn't know. She wished her old friends were not so far away.

"Just look at those magnificent mountains," said her mother. "I'm sure we're going to love living in this town."

"Who do you think could have left those dandelions yesterday?"
Anna asked.

"Maybe they were left for someone who lived in the house before us. Perhaps a little girl's friends don't know she has moved away," answered her mother.

The house was nearly tidy the next day, but Anna's mother was still busy.

Anna drew a picture to send to one of her old friends.

"It's no fun without any friends to play with," she said sadly.
But what was that? Anna heard the same quiet tip tap sound!

Anna rushed to the letter box, and this time she saw a letter in it! There was no name on the envelope, but inside there was a short message written in big letters.

Friends are nice
I'm very happy you
have come
I'll be waiting

Anna read the letter again and again. "I'm sure this letter is for me," she thought.

Anna enjoyed visiting her new school. A friendly teacher showed her all the toys the children played with, and told her about the meadow at the foot of the mountains where the children sometimes played.

"You'll soon make lots of new friends," the teacher told Anna. Anna looked at all the children laughing and chattering in the playground. She hoped that one of them had sent her the letter.

"Violets, dandelions, a letter . . .
Violets, dandelions, a letter . . ."
Anna sang as she played marbles by herself. How she longed for someone to play with!

Just then she heard that sound again — a quiet little tip tap noise at the front door.

"Wait! Wait!" Anna shouted in her loudest voice as she rushed to the front door. She saw something coming through the letter box! It was a beautiful paper doll.

Anna grabbed the doll and quickly opened the door. She saw a little girl just going out of the gate.
"Wait! Wait!" Anna shouted again.

The little girl turned around slowly. Her cheeks were bright red.

Anna walked down the path.
"Those violets — were they for me?" she asked.
The little girl nodded.
"And . . . and the letter? Was that for me too?" Once again the little girl nodded.
Anna looked down at the beautifully folded paper doll in her hand.
All for her! The little girl looked at Anna shyly and said in a very small voice, "Will you play with me?"
This time it was Anna who nodded, so both girls smiled happily and went off to play.

# How To Make Friends

Anna was new in her neighborhood and her school. If there was a new person in your neighborhood or class, how could you help that person feel more at home?

Write your ideas down and make a how-to book called "How To Be a Friend." Draw pictures to illustrate your ideas. Then share your how-to book with a friend.

## Meet the Authors and Illustrators

Pat Cummings writes about people that she knows and places that she's been. The idea for the story *Jimmy Lee Did It* came from a make-believe friend that her brother had when he was little. This make-believe friend was always blamed for things in the Cummings house. Before Pat Cummings draws pictures for her books, she reads her stories to children. Then she asks them what they picture in their minds. This helps her decide what pictures to draw for her stories.

**K**evin Henkes began writing and illustrating when he was a teenager. Since then, he has written many fine picture books like *Bailey Goes Camping*. He has also written some longer books for older children.

**Y**oriko Tsutsui lives in Japan with her husband and three daughters. This author writes in Japanese, but some of her stories are printed in English for English-speaking children to enjoy.

**A**kiko Hayashi has illustrated many books by Yoriko Tsutsui and other authors. She has also written and illustrated many children's books of her own.

# More Problems to Solve!

**Jamaica Tag-Along** *by Juanita Havill*
Jamaica can't understand why her big brother doesn't want her to tag along after him. Then someone begins to tag along after her.

**My Dog and the Knock Knock Mystery**
*by David A. Adler*
Jennie's friend Billy is bothered by a mysterious knocking. Luckily Jennie's dog is a detective.

**Molly Pink** *by Judith Caseley*
Molly loves to sing so much her brother calls her Birdy. But what goes wrong when she tries to sing away from home?

**Hemi's Pet** *by Joan de Hamel*
Hemi's problem is that he doesn't have a pet. So how can he be in his school pet show without one?

# Glossary

## A

**attach** When you **attach** things, you put them together: Tim is **attaching** a basket to his bicycle so he will be able to carry his books.

**attic** An **attic** is a room at the top of some houses: My grandmother keeps things she doesn't use a lot in her **attic**.

**birthday** Jenny is seven years old. She will be eight on her next **birthday**.

---

**bricks** **Bricks** are made from clay. They are used in buildings, walkways, and walls: Tim's father made their house of **bricks**.

---

**bubbling** The water in the pot is **bubbling** because it is very hot.

**build** When you **build** a house, you make a house: I like to watch the workers **build** the new house on our street.

**camping** When you go **camping,** you sleep and cook outside: The girls are **camping** in the woods.

**capture** When you **capture** something, you catch it: The police will **capture** the robbers and put them in jail.

**chimney** A **chimney** is part of a house: When you have a fire in your fireplace, the smoke goes out the **chimney**.

**crystal** A **crystal** is a pretty, clear piece of rock, ice, or glass: Sometimes ice forms **crystals** on my windows.

**describe** When you **describe** something, you tell what it looks like: Pat doesn't know what your dog looks like. Can you **describe** it to her?

**envelope** You put a letter into an **envelope** before you mail it: Danny put an address and a stamp on the **envelope**.

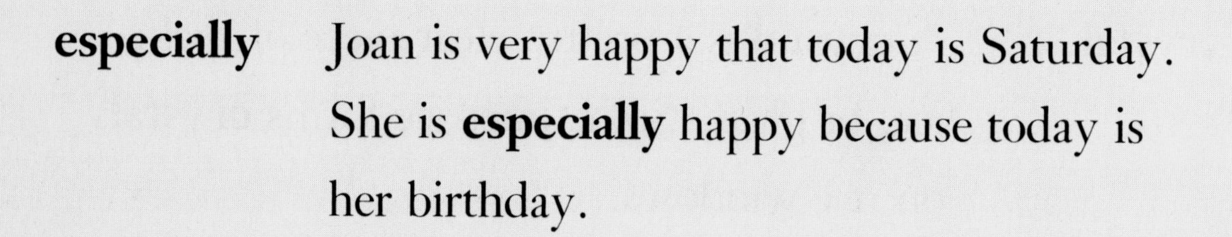

**especially** Joan is very happy that today is Saturday. She is **especially** happy because today is her birthday.

# F

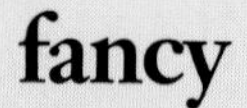

**fancy** People might say "**Fancy** that!" instead of "Can you believe that!" or "Imagine that!": In the story a man makes soup from a stone. Can you **fancy** that?

**fishing** People use a rod and a reel when they go **fishing:** Grandpa is **fishing** on the lake. He will catch some fish for supper.

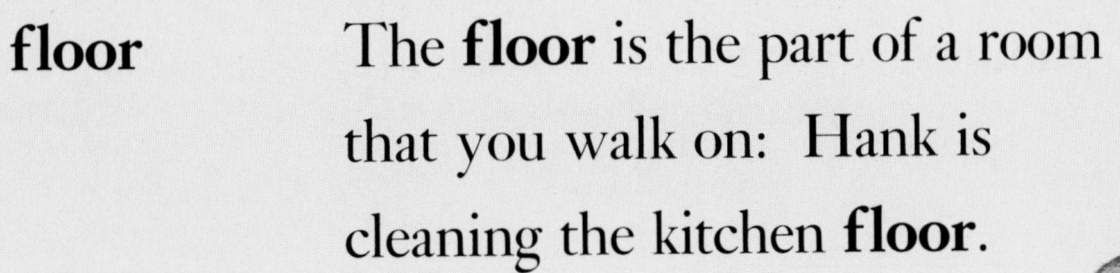

**floor** The **floor** is the part of a room that you walk on: Hank is cleaning the kitchen **floor**.

**gray** You can make **gray** paint by mixing black and white.

## H

**hive** A bee's home is called a **hive:** Some bees built their **hive** in our tree.

**huff** When you **huff** you blow out a big breath: Lisa **huffed** and **huffed** to blow out the candles.

## I

**idea** An **idea** is a thought: At first Jack didn't know what to do. But then he had a great **idea**!

**important** Pete wants very much to run in the race. Running in the race is **important** to him.

## J

**jacket** A **jacket** is a short coat. You wear a **jacket** to keep you warm.

**juicy** These are **juicy** oranges. Maybe we can make orange juice from them.

## K

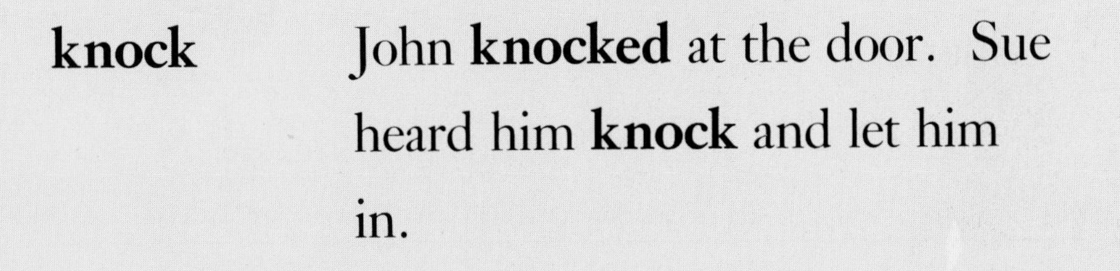

**knock** John **knocked** at the door. Sue heard him **knock** and let him in.

## L

**library** A **library** is a building that has lots of books for people to borrow: Anne got three big books at the **library**.

**marbles** **Marbles** are small, round balls made of stone or glass. They are used in games: Jerry played a game of **marbles** with Sharon.

---

**message** A **message** can be a short letter, a note, or something that someone tells you: Fred wrote me a **message**. He asked me to meet him at the park on Monday.

**minute** You use **minutes** to tell the time: "What time is it?" asked Carlos. "It is one **minute** past five," said Tom.

---

**mountains** **Mountains** are very high hills: We hiked up to the top of the **mountain** and looked down. Everything below looked so small!

---

**mystery** A **mystery** is something that is not known: Margo's coat just disappeared! What happened to it is a **mystery**.

**nothing** Pat looked at a lot of clothes in the store but she saw **nothing** she liked. So, she didn't buy anything at all.

**open** The box is closed. What do you think we will see when we **open** it?

**package** Nancy got a big **package** in the mail. She opened it to see what was inside.

**quietly** When you do something **quietly,** you don't make much noise: Jerry came into the room so **quietly** that we didn't know he was there.

**radio** At night I turn on my small **radio** and listen to music and news.

---

**replied** When you **reply,** you give an answer to a question: "What day is today?" asked Tim. "It's Monday," **replied** Beth.

---

**roasting** Jane is **roasting** the marshmallows over the hot fire. Soon they will be brown outside.

**shoe** You wear a **shoe** on your foot: Jean put on her socks and **shoes**.

**stick** A **stick** is a small piece of wood: Tony throws the **sticks**. Then his dog brings them back.

**storm** A **storm** is when it rains or snows very hard: It snowed all day Monday. We stayed home because of the **storm**.

**straw** **Straw** looks like dry grass or stems: Hats and baskets can be made from **straw**.

**tent** A **tent** is a cover for people. It is made from cloth and is held up with poles and ropes: The boys set up their **tent** in the back yard so they could sleep outside.

**tomorrow** The day after today is **tomorrow:** Today is Friday. There is no school **tomorrow** because it is Saturday.

**tongue** You have a **tongue** in your mouth. You use your **tongue** when you eat and when you talk.

**trouble** My puppy behaves most of the time. When she doesn't behave and causes lots of **trouble,** I send her to the doghouse.

**unfamiliar** Tim had never been to the city. He had never seen tall buildings or crowds of people before. The city looked strange and **unfamiliar** to him.

**violets** **Violets** are flowers: Sam bought some purple **violets** at the plant store.

**wolf** A **wolf** is a wild animal that looks like a dog.

**young** Sara is **young**. She is only two years old.

## Acknowledgments


For each of the selections listed below, grateful acknowledgment is made for permission to excerpt and/or reprint original or copyrighted material, as follows:

### Major Selections

"Anna's Secret Friend," by Yoriko Tsutsui. Text copyright © 1986 Yoriko Tsutsui. Illustrations copyright © 1986 Akiko Hayashi. Reprinted by permission of Viking Penguin, a division of Penguin Books USA, Inc., and Fukuinkan Shoten, Publishers, Inc.

"Bailey Goes Camping," by Kevin Henkes, copyright © 1985 by Kevin Henkes. Reprinted by permission of Greenwillow Books, a division of William Morrow and Co., Inc.

Illustration by Tomie dePaola of "The Dog and His Shadow," by Aesop from *Tomie dePaola's Favorite Nursery Tales*, copyright © 1986 by Tomie dePaola. Reprinted by permission of G. P. Putnam's Sons.

"Geraldine's Big Snow," by Holly Keller, copyright © 1988 by Holly Keller. Reprinted by permission of Greenwillow Books, a division of William Morrow and Co., Inc.

"Jimmy Lee Did It," by Pat Cummings, copyright © 1985 by Pat Cummings. Reprinted by permission of Lothrop, Lee and Shepard Books, a division of William Morrow and Co., Inc.

"My Five Senses," by Aliki (Thomas Y. Crowell), copyright © 1962, 1989 by Aliki Brandenberg. Reprinted by permission of Harper and Row, Publishers, Inc.

"Stone Soup," by Ann McGovern, text copyright © 1968 by Ann McGovern. Reprinted by permission of Scholastic, Inc.

"The Surprise," by George Shannon, illustrated by Jose Aruego and Ariane Dewey. Text copyright © 1983 by George Shannon. Illustrations copyright © 1983 by Jose Aruego and Ariane Dewey. Reprinted by permission of Greenwillow Books (A division of William Morrow and Co.)

"This Old Man, The Counting Song," illustrated by Robin Michal Koontz, illustrations copyright © 1988 by Robin Michal Koontz. Reprinted by permission of G. P. Putnam's Sons.

"The Three Little Pigs," by Paul Galdone. Copyright © 1970 by Paul Galdone. Reprinted by permission of Clarion Books/Ticknor and Fields, a Houghton Mifflin Company.

### Poetry

"The Bridge," from *Is Somewhere Always Far Away?* Copyright © 1967 by Leland B. Jacobs. Reprinted by permission of Henry Holt and Company Inc.

"Bus Stop," from *Is Somewhere Always Far Away?* Copyright © 1967 by Leland B. Jacobs. Reprinted by permission of Henry Holt and Company Inc.

"The Old Woman," from *Appley Dappley's Nursery Rhymes* by Beatrix Potter. Copyright © 1917 by Frederick Warne and Co. Reprinted by permission of Frederick Warne and Co.

"A Problem," from *Rhymes About Us* by Marchette Chute. Copyright © 1974 by E. P. Dutton. Reprinted by permission of Mary Chute Smith.

"Shoe Laces," from *Is Somewhere Always Far Away?* by Leland Jacobs. Copyright © 1967 by Leland B. Jacobs. Reprinted by permission.

"The Subway Train," from *Is Somewhere Always Far Away?* Copyright © 1967 by Leland B. Jacobs. Reprinted by permission of Henry Holt and Company, Inc.

"Whistling," from *Rainy Rainy Saturday* by Jack Prelutsky. Copyright © 1980 by Jack Prelutsky. Reprinted by permission of Greenwillow Books (a division of William Morrow and Co.)

### Theme Books

The Theme Books shown on pages 76, 144, and 200 are available from Houghton Mifflin Company. They are reprinted with permission from various publishers or distributed through the Trade Division of Houghton Mifflin Company. Jacket artists for these books are listed below.

*The Great Sea Monster, or A Book by You*, by Berthe Amoss. Jacket art by Berthe Amoss, copyright © 1975 by Berthe Amoss.

*Jamaica Tag-Along*, by Juanita Havill. Jacket art by Anne Sibley O'Brien, copyright © 1989 by Anne Sibley O'Brien.

*The Princess and the Pea*, by Hans Christian Andersen, translated by Anthea Bell. Jacket art by Eve Tharlet, copyright © 1987 by Neugebauer Press.

### Additional Recommended Reading

Houghton Mifflin Company wishes to thank the following publishers for permission to reproduce their book covers on pages 76, 77, 144, 145, 200 and 201.

Thomas Y. Crowell Junior Books, an imprint of Harper & Row, Publishers, Inc.:
*My Visit to the Dinosaurs*, by Aliki. Jacket art by Aliki Brandenberg, copyright © 1969, 1985 by Aliki Brandenberg. Published simultaneously in Canada by Fitzhenry & Whiteside Limited, Toronto.

Greenwillow Books, a division of William Morrow & Company, Inc.:
*At Mary Bloom's*, by Aliki. Jacket art by Aliki Brandenberg, copyright © 1976 by Aliki Brandenberg.

*Dance Away*, by George Shannon. Jacket art by Jose Aruego and Ariane Dewey, copyright © 1982 by Jose Aruego and Ariane Dewey. *Lizzie's Invitation*, by Holly Keller. Jacket art by Holly Keller, copyright © 1987 by Holly Keller. *Molly Pink*, by Judith Caseley. Jacket art by Judith Caseley, copyright © 1985 by Judith Caseley.

Holiday House:

*My Dog and the Knock Knock Mystery*, by David A. Adler. Jacket art by Marsha Winborn, copyright © 1985 by Marsha Winborn.

Houghton Mifflin Company:

*Hemi's Pet*, by Joan de Hamel. Jacket art by Christine Ross, copyright © 1985 by Christine Ross. First published in New Zealand by Reed Methuen Publishers, Ltd., Auckland. *Old MacDonald Had a Farm*, retold by Carol Jones. Jacket art by Carol Jones, copyright © 1988 by Carol Jones.

The Seabury Press:

*Little Tuppen*, by Paul Galdone. Jacket art by Paul Galdone, copyright © 1979 by Paul Galdone.

Viking Kestrel, a division of Penguin Books USA, Inc.:

*Each Peach Pear Plum*, by Janet and Allan Ahlberg. Jacket art by Janet and Allan Ahlberg, copyright © 1978 by Janet and Allan Ahlberg. First published in Great Britain by Penguin Books Ltd.

## Credits

**Program design** Carbone Smolan Associates

**Cover design** Carbone Smolan Associates

**Design 10–77** Waters Design Associates; **78–145** WGBH; **146–201** DeFrancis Studio

**Illustrations 10–13** Mary Lynn Blasutta; **14–31** Aliki; **32–57** Jose Aruego and Ariane Dewey; **58–68** Holly Keller; **69** Karen Bell; **70–71** Holly Keller; **72–77** Mary Lynn Blasutta; **78–81** Cat Bowman Smith; **82–96** Robin Michal Koontz; **97** Tomie dePaola; **98–118** Cat Bowman Smith; **120–121** Robin Spowart; **122–141** Paul Galdone; **143–145** Kevin O'Malley; **146–149** Chris Demarest; **150–162** Pat Cummings; **163** Chris Demarest; **164–167** Chris Reed; **168–178** Kevin Henkes; **179** Chris Demarest; **180–181** Chris Reed; **182–196** Akiko Hayashi; **197** Chris Demarest; **198** Pat Cummings; **199** (top) Kevin Henkes, (bottom) Akiko Hayashi; **200–201** Chris Demarest; **202** (top), **204, 206, 207** (top), **209** (bottom), **210** (top), **213** (bottom), **214** (bottom) Susan Miller; **202** (bottom), **203** (bottom), **207** (middle), **208, 210** (bottom), **212, 214** (top), **217** (top) Jan Pyk; **203** (top), **205, 207** (bottom), **209** (top), **211, 213** (top), **215, 217** (bottom) Lorretta Lustig

**Photography 12** (right) David Holter, (top left) Ian Bradshaw, (bottom left) Michal Heron; **13** (right) Richard Bowditch, (left) courtesy of Holly Keller; **30** Alexa Brandenberg; **31** courtesy of Aliki Brandenberg; **54** David Holter; **55** Michal Heron; **56** (right) Michal Heron, (left) A.T. Atwell/The Image Bank; **57** (top) C. Moore/The Image Bank, (bottom) Michal Heron; **70–71** David Arky; **71** Barry Keller; **72** Richard Bowditch; **96** Keith Ayres/courtesy Robin Michal Koontz; **119** (top left) photo by Michael Ortiz, courtesy of Macmillan Publishing Company, (bottom right) Sue Smith; **142** photo by Suzanne Opton, courtesy of Clarion Books, a Houghton Mifflin Company

**End Matter** layout design by Publicom, Inc.